Dingo

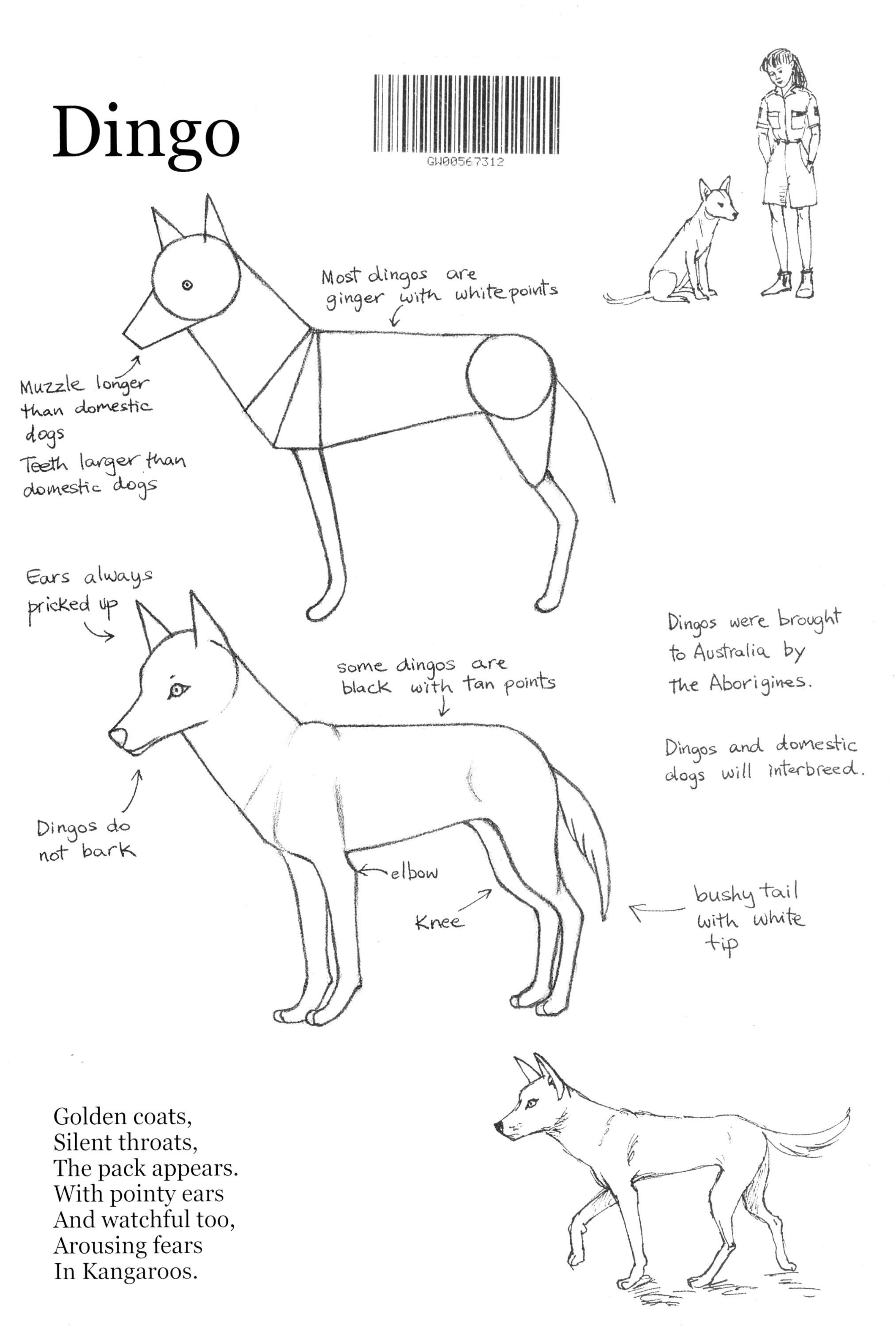

GW00567312

Most dingos are ginger with white points

Muzzle longer than domestic dogs
Teeth larger than domestic dogs

Ears always pricked up

some dingos are black with tan points

Dingos do not bark

Dingos were brought to Australia by the Aborigines.

Dingos and domestic dogs will interbreed.

elbow

Knee

bushy tail with white tip

Golden coats,
Silent throats,
The pack appears.
With pointy ears
And watchful too,
Arousing fears
In Kangaroos.

Red Kangaroo

Boxing! Yes, they really do!
They arrange a show for you.
Up on their tails they kick and punch.
But they'll be dozing after lunch.

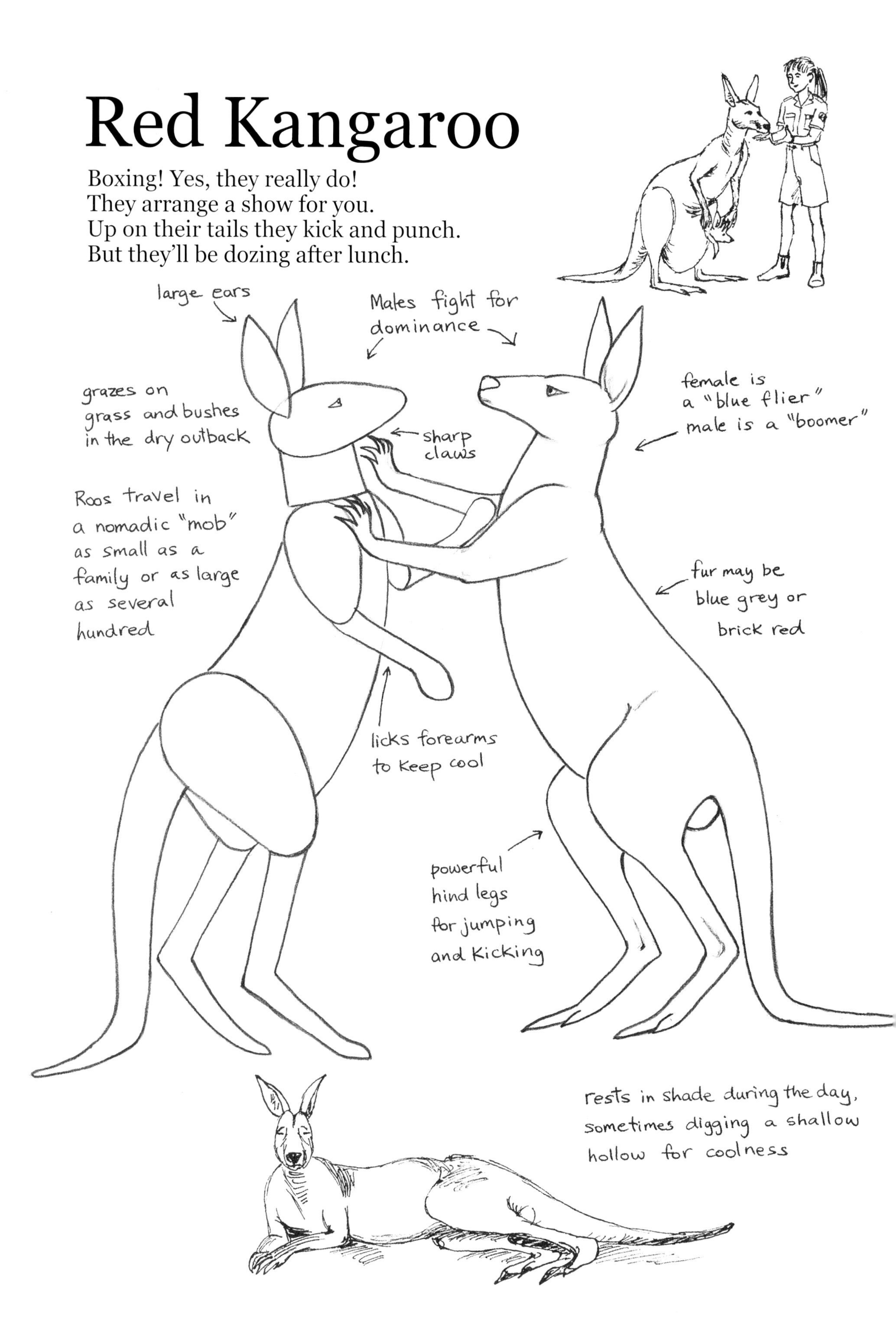

large ears

Males fight for dominance

grazes on grass and bushes in the dry outback

female is a "blue flier" male is a "boomer"

sharp claws

Roos travel in a nomadic "mob" as small as a family or as large as several hundred

fur may be blue grey or brick red

licks forearms to keep cool

powerful hind legs for jumping and kicking

rests in shade during the day, sometimes digging a shallow hollow for coolness

Bennett's Wallaby

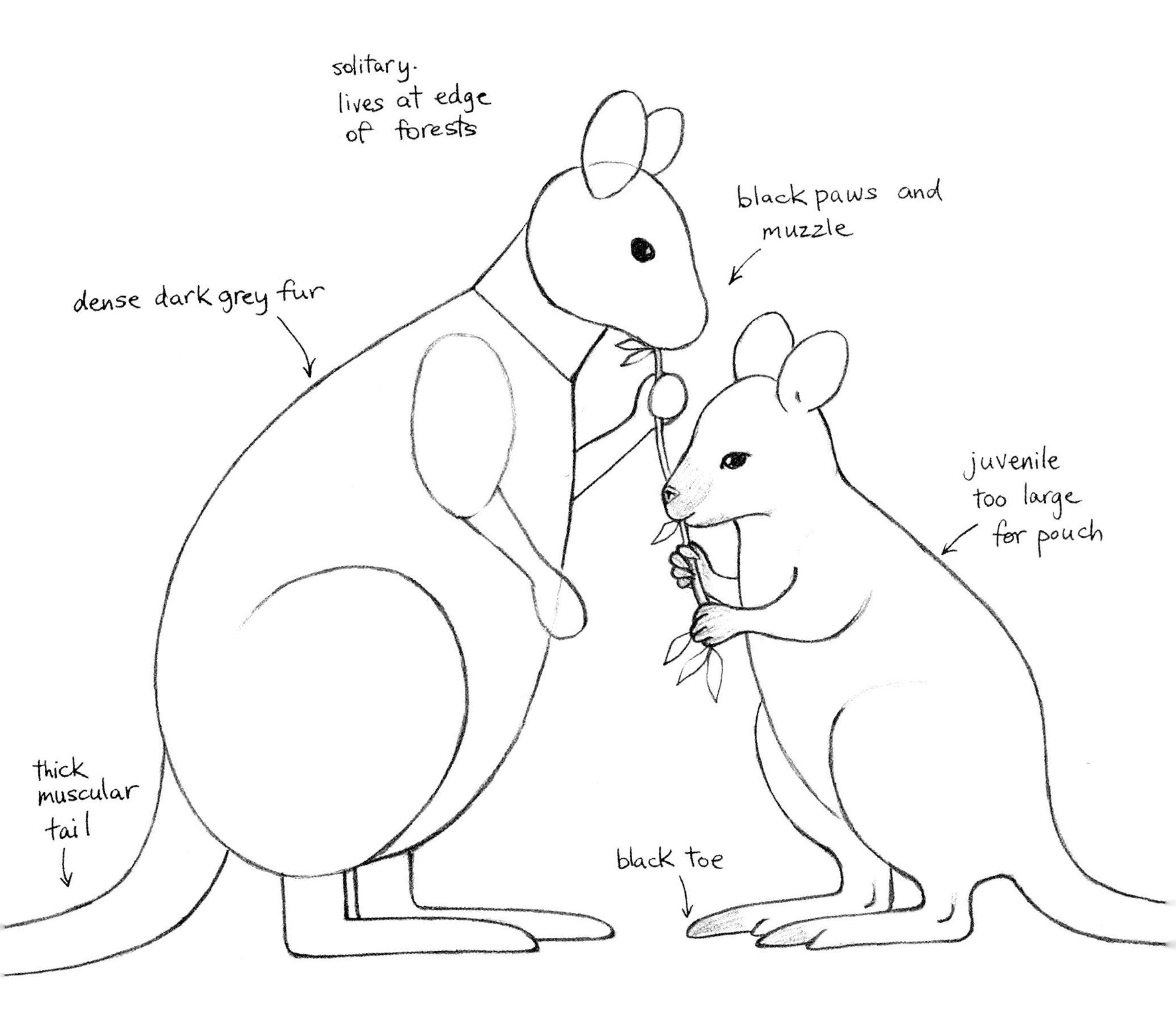

solitary.
lives at edge
of forests

black paws and
muzzle

dense dark grey fur

juvenile
too large
for pouch

thick
muscular
tail

black toe

Her joey takes a longer ride
Than other roos who ride inside.
Mum keeps him there for company.
She's otherwise quite solitary.

Quokka

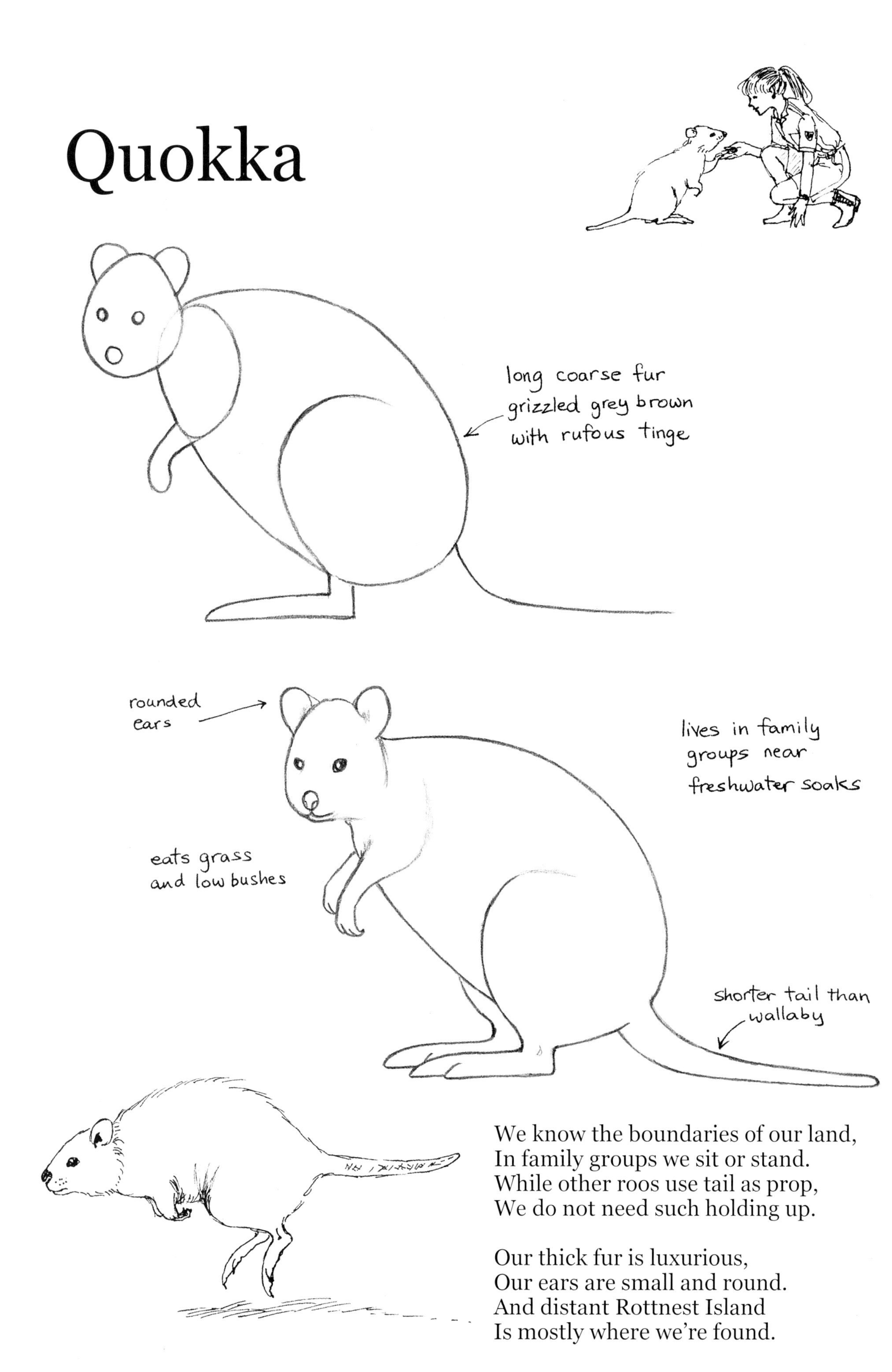

long coarse fur
grizzled grey brown
with rufous tinge

rounded
ears

lives in family
groups near
freshwater soaks

eats grass
and low bushes

shorter tail than
wallaby

We know the boundaries of our land,
In family groups we sit or stand.
While other roos use tail as prop,
We do not need such holding up.

Our thick fur is luxurious,
Our ears are small and round.
And distant Rottnest Island
Is mostly where we're found.

Boongarry
(Lumholtz's Tree Kangaroo)

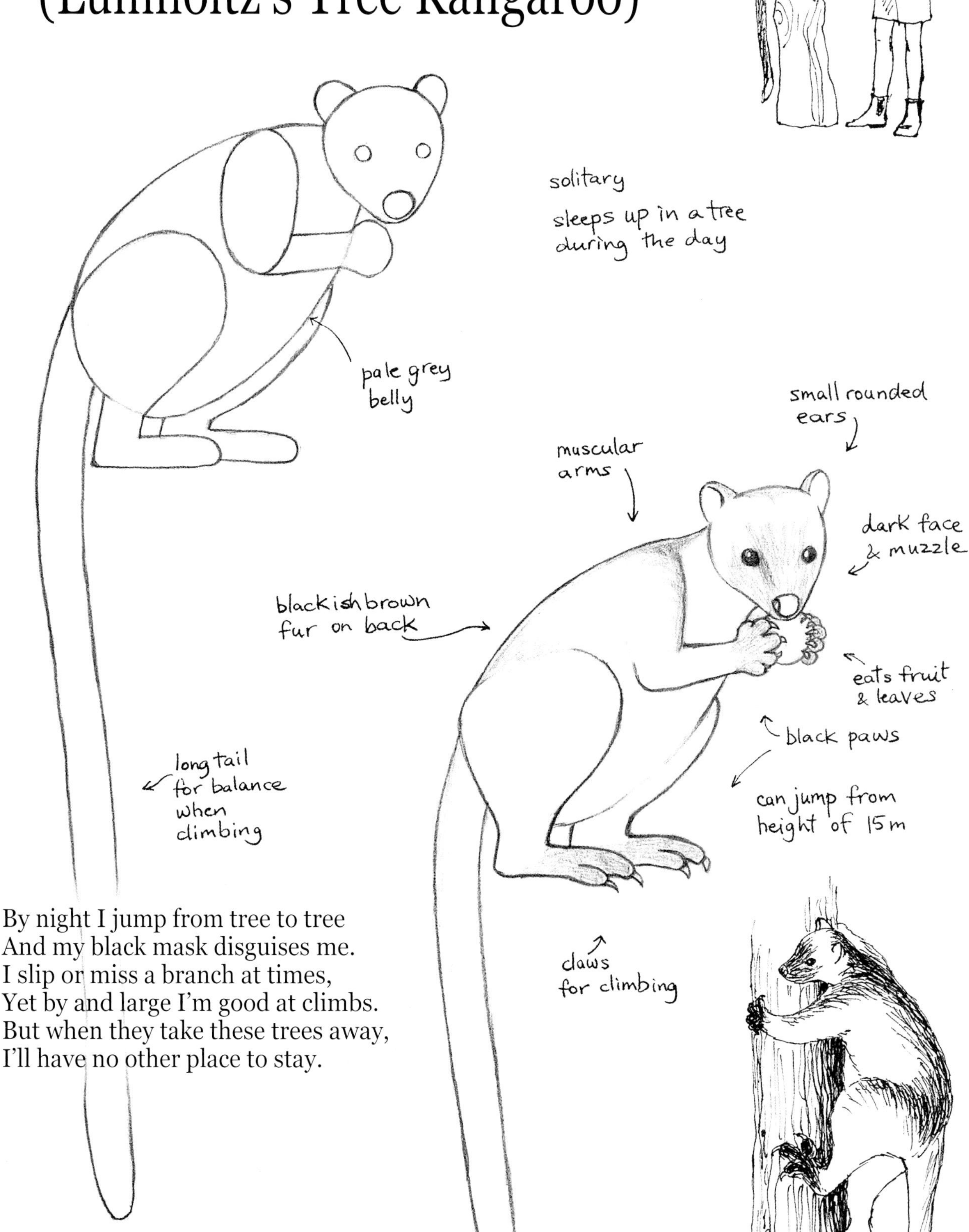

solitary

sleeps up in a tree during the day

pale grey belly

muscular arms

small rounded ears

dark face & muzzle

blackish brown fur on back

eats fruit & leaves

black paws

can jump from height of 15 m

long tail for balance when climbing

claws for climbing

By night I jump from tree to tree
And my black mask disguises me.
I slip or miss a branch at times,
Yet by and large I'm good at climbs.
But when they take these trees away,
I'll have no other place to stay.

Spinifex Hopping Mouse

large ears

light brown fur

grey white belly

long hind legs

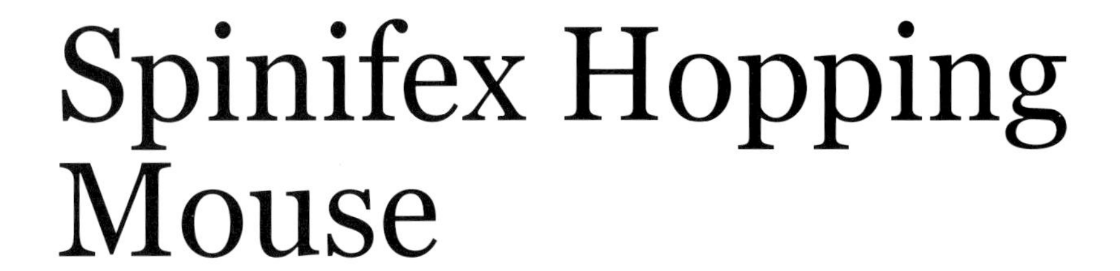

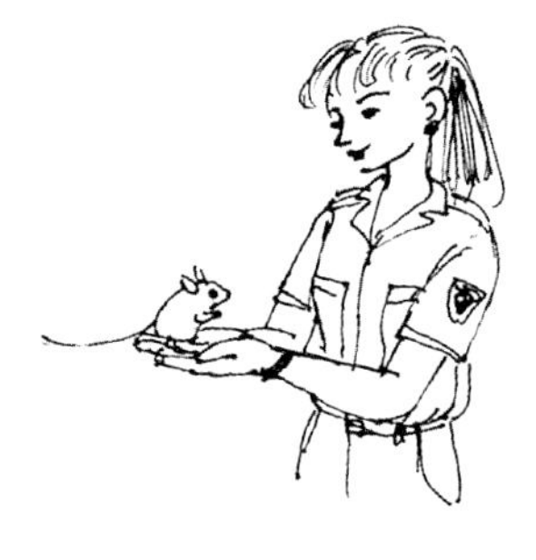

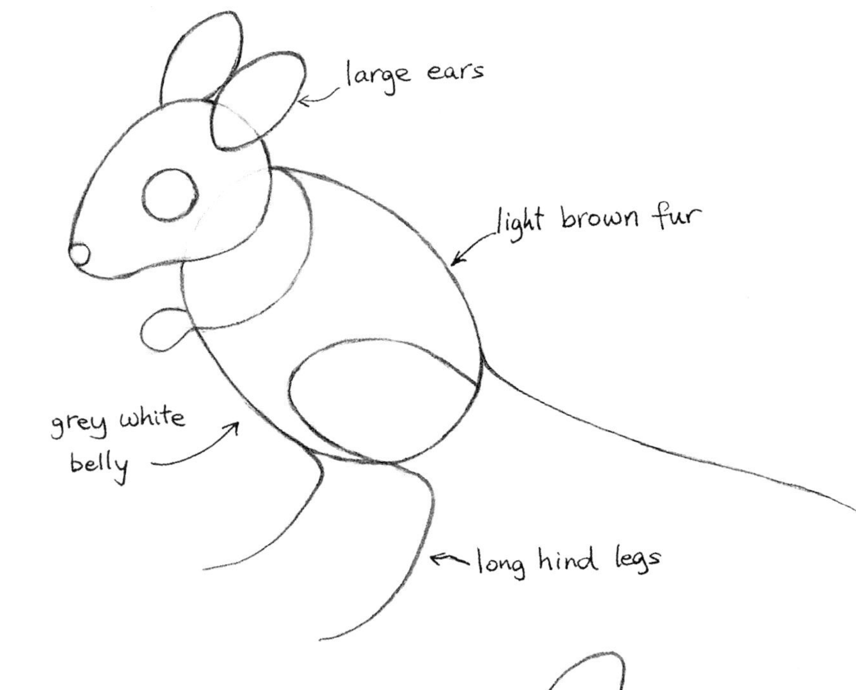

lives in family groups
in deep burrows
in arid zones of central
& western Australia

survives
without drinking

eats seeds, insects,
roots & shoots

hops with long tufted
tail extended

My neighbours are marsupials
But I'm a kind of mouse.
A tunnel dug below the ground
Is my answer for a house.

My tail is like a paint brush
With a sort of feathered end.
And where I live it's very dry,
Beneath a paint blue desert sky.

Pebble Mound Mouse

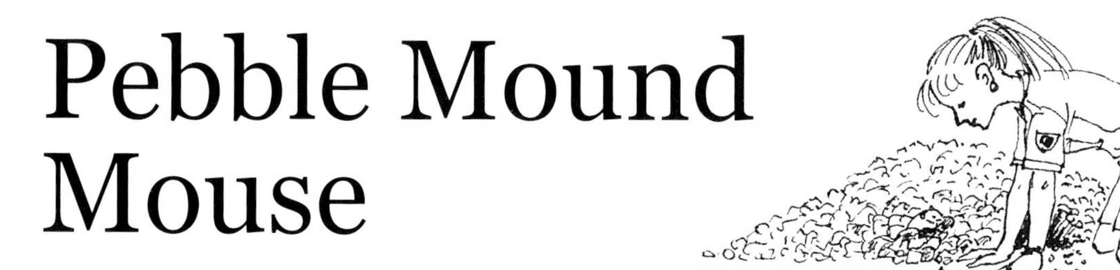

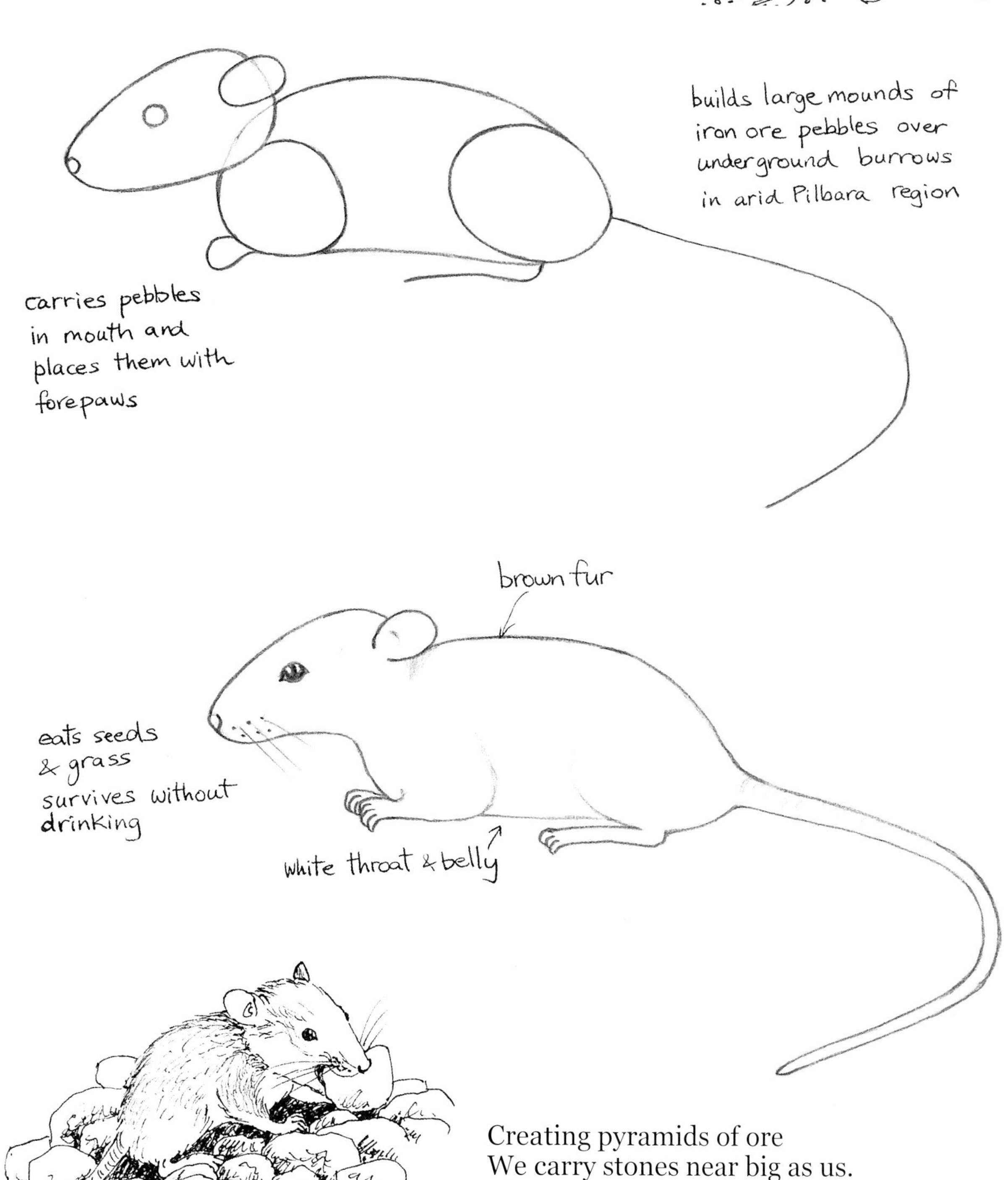

builds large mounds of
iron ore pebbles over
underground burrows
in arid Pilbara region

carries pebbles
in mouth and
places them with
forepaws

brown fur

eats seeds
& grass
survives without
drinking

white throat & belly

Creating pyramids of ore
We carry stones near big as us.
Then hopping down the slopes for more,
We pile them on with little fuss.
Our house is called a pebble mound.
And now we're resting underground.

Little Pygmy Possum

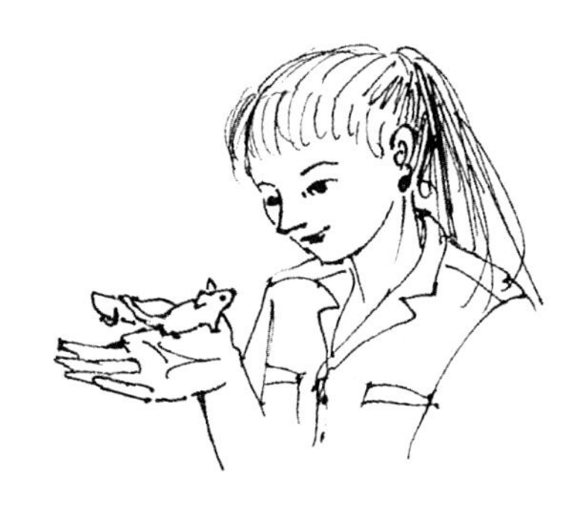

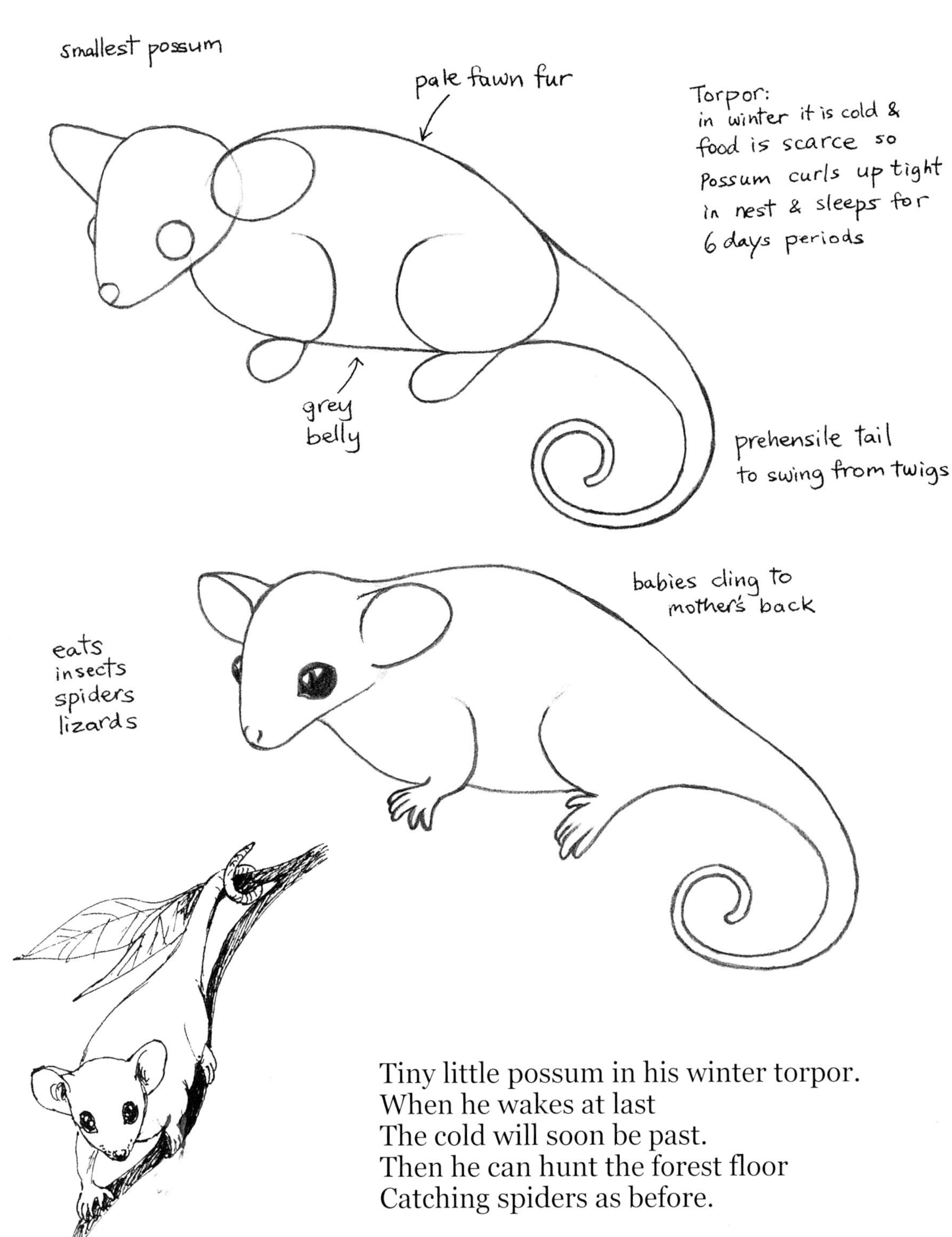

smallest possum

pale fawn fur

Torpor:
in winter it is cold &
food is scarce so
Possum curls up tight
in nest & sleeps for
6 days periods

grey
belly

prehensile tail
to swing from twigs

babies cling to
mother's back

eats
insects
spiders
lizards

Tiny little possum in his winter torpor.
When he wakes at last
The cold will soon be past.
Then he can hunt the forest floor
Catching spiders as before.

Long Tailed Planigale

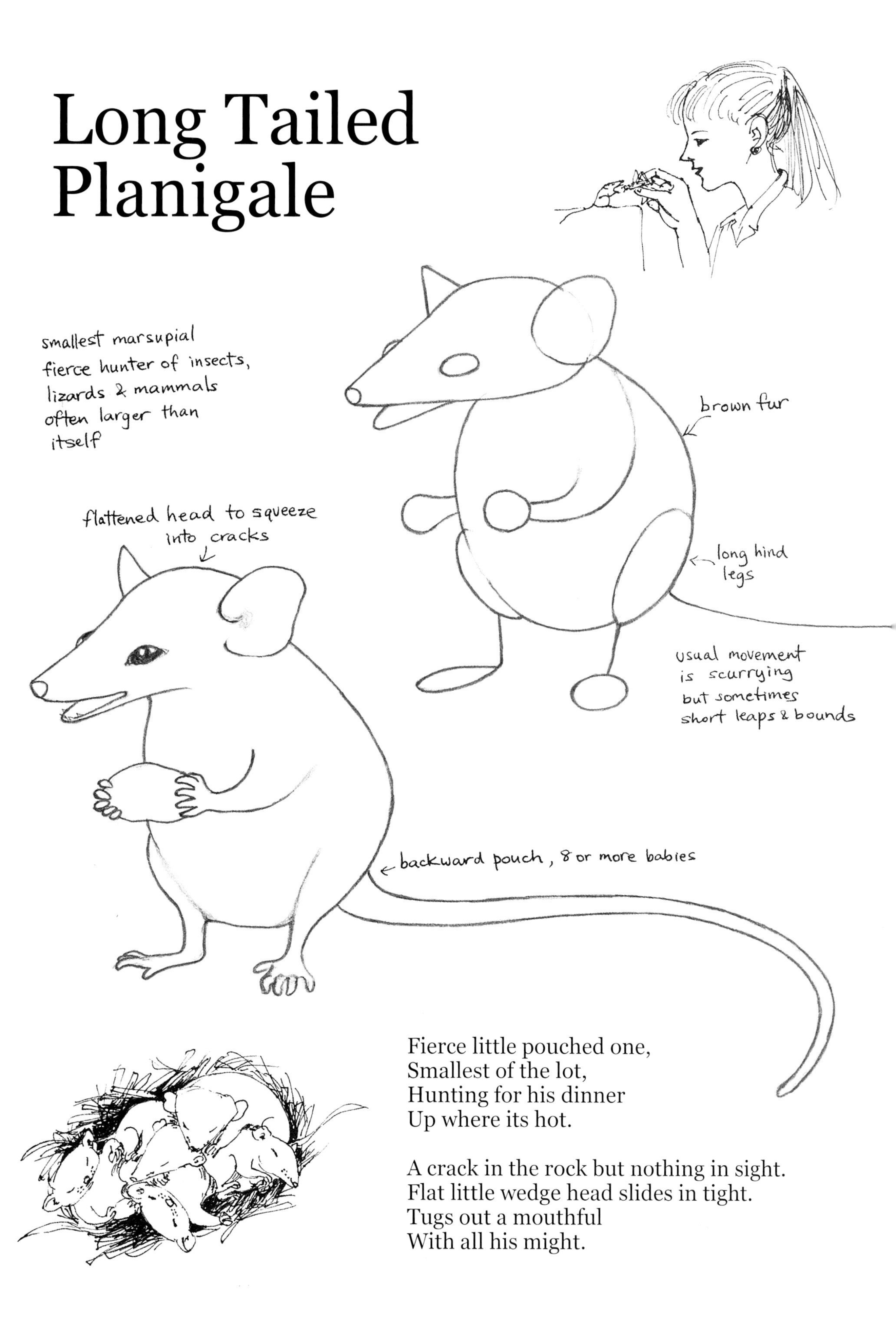

smallest marsupial
fierce hunter of insects,
lizards & mammals
often larger than
itself

brown fur

flattened head to squeeze
into cracks

long hind
legs

usual movement
is scurrying
but sometimes
short leaps & bounds

← backward pouch, 8 or more babies

Fierce little pouched one,
Smallest of the lot,
Hunting for his dinner
Up where its hot.

A crack in the rock but nothing in sight.
Flat little wedge head slides in tight.
Tugs out a mouthful
With all his might.

Australian Fur Seal

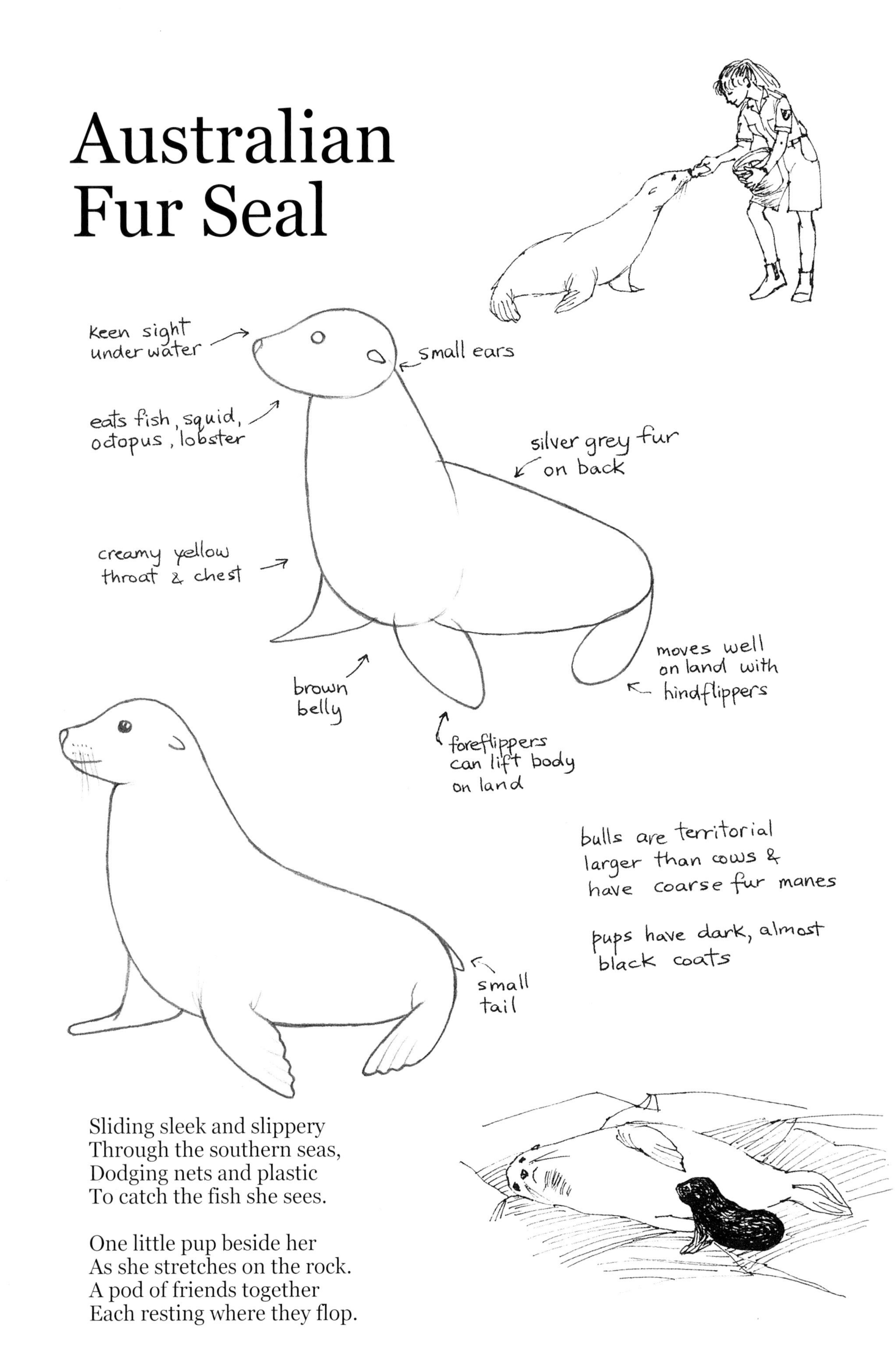

keen sight under water

small ears

eats fish, squid, octopus, lobster

silver grey fur on back

creamy yellow throat & chest

brown belly

foreflippers can lift body on land

moves well on land with hindflippers

small tail

bulls are territorial larger than cows & have coarse fur manes

pups have dark, almost black coats

Sliding sleek and slippery
Through the southern seas,
Dodging nets and plastic
To catch the fish she sees.

One little pup beside her
As she stretches on the rock.
A pod of friends together
Each resting where they flop.

Bottlenose Dolphin

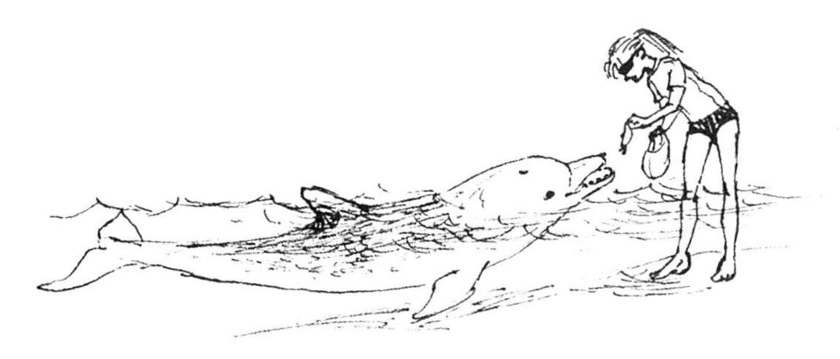

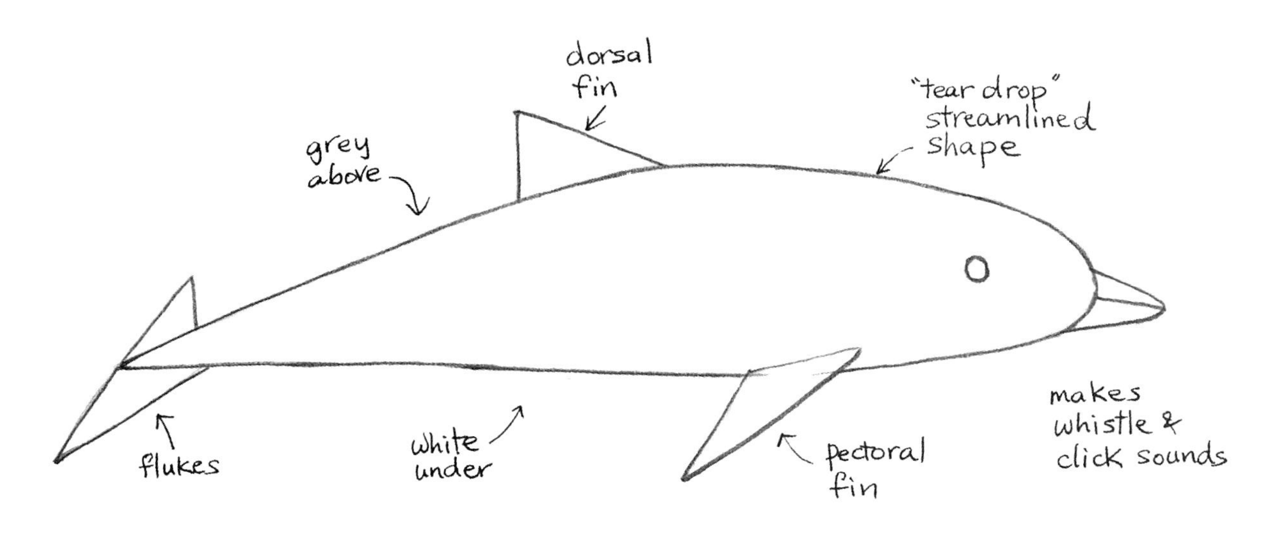

dorsal fin

grey above

"tear drop" streamlined shape

flukes

white under

pectoral fin

makes whistle & click sounds

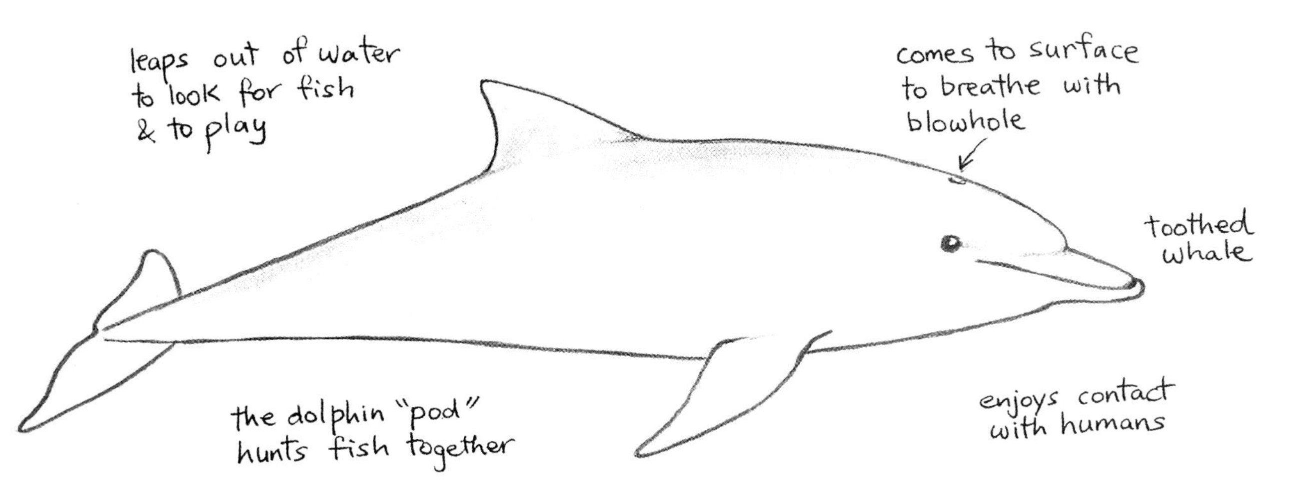

leaps out of water to look for fish & to play

comes to surface to breathe with blowhole

toothed whale

the dolphin "pod" hunts fish together

enjoys contact with humans

Talking in clicks and whistles,
Cousins of the whale,
They're sometimes right beside us
When we're going for a sail.

Arcing through the ocean,
Up beside the prow,
See the perfect streamline motion
That their fine physique allows.

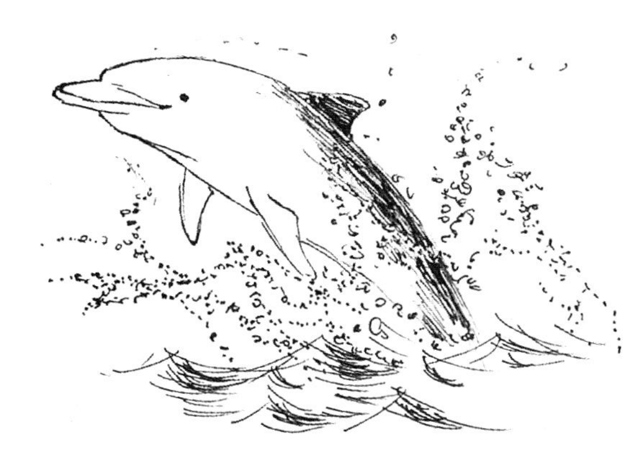

Perentie
(Goanna)

Tail lashing
Rival bashing
The fight unfurls
To win the rights
To lizard girls.

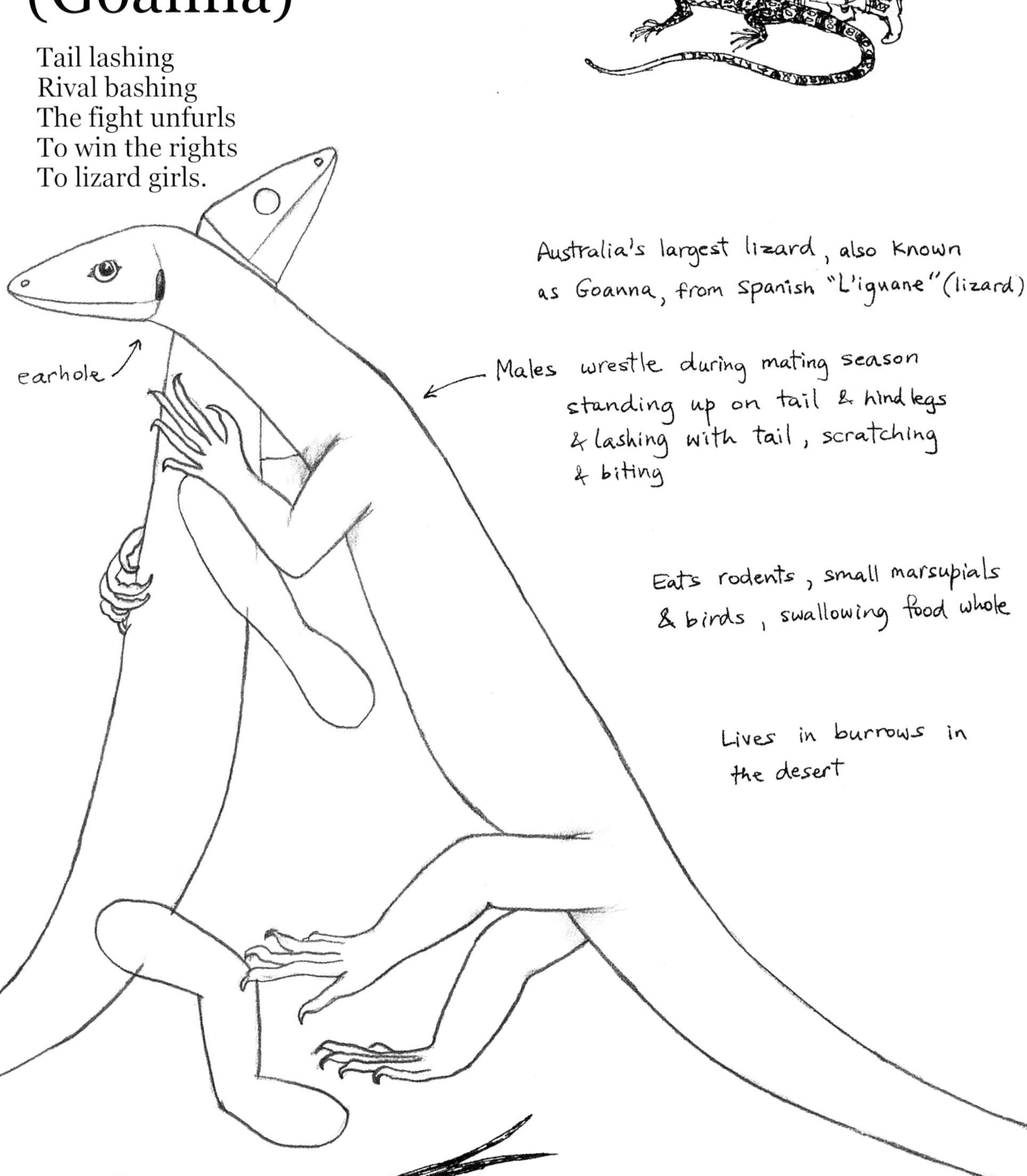

Australia's largest lizard, also known
as Goanna, from Spanish "L'iguane"(lizard)

Males wrestle during mating season
standing up on tail & hind legs
& lashing with tail, scratching
& biting

Eats rodents, small marsupials
& birds, swallowing food whole

Lives in burrows in
the desert

earhole

long forked tongue
picks up scent particles
in the air & takes them
to Jacobson's Organ
on roof of mouth

Saltwater Crocodile

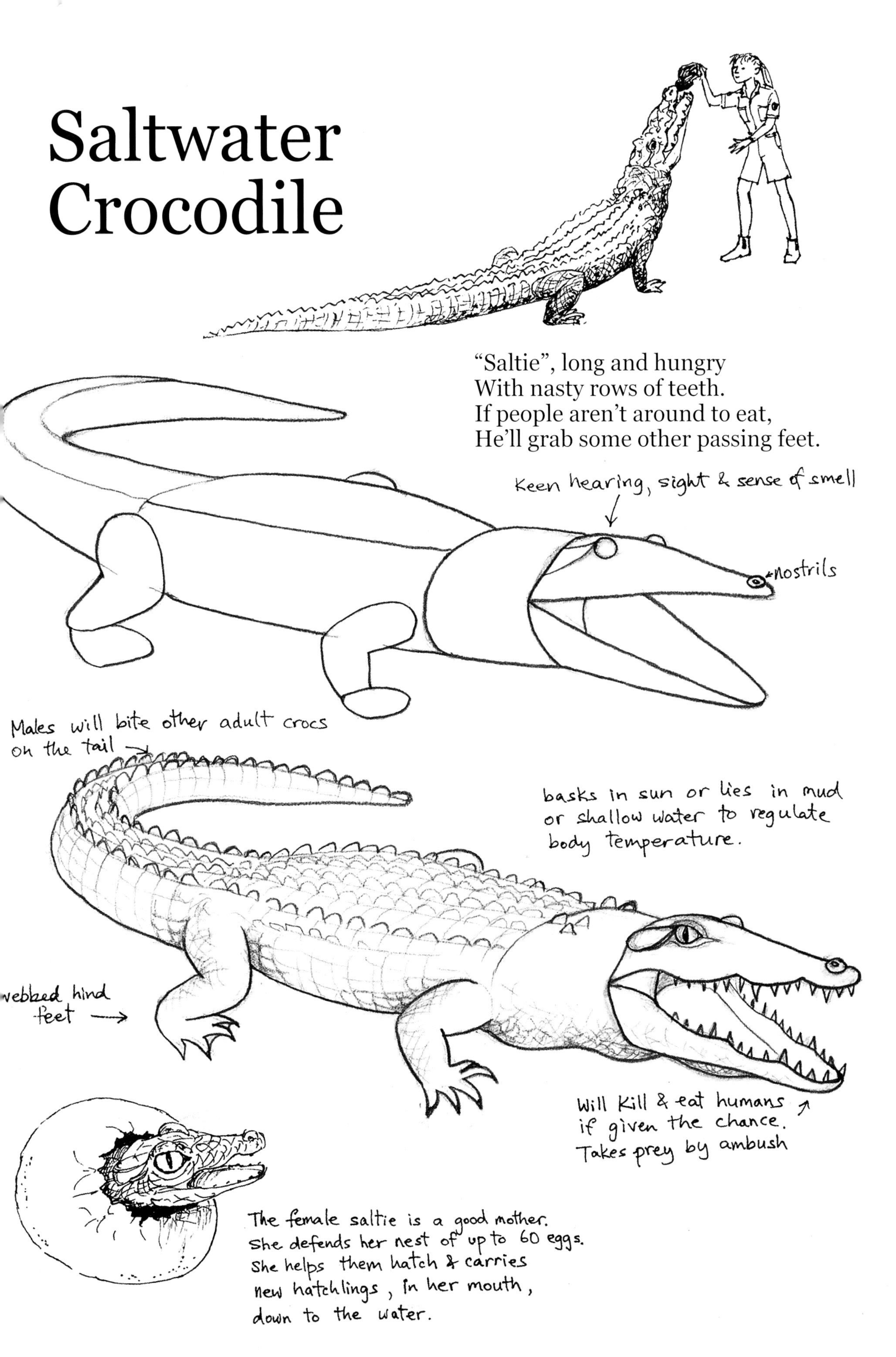

"Saltie", long and hungry
With nasty rows of teeth.
If people aren't around to eat,
He'll grab some other passing feet.

Keen hearing, sight & sense of smell

←Nostrils

Males will bite other adult crocs on the tail →

basks in sun or lies in mud or shallow water to regulate body temperature.

webbed hind feet →

Will kill & eat humans ↗
if given the chance.
Takes prey by ambush

The female saltie is a good mother.
She defends her nest of up to 60 eggs.
She helps them hatch & carries
new hatchlings, in her mouth,
down to the water.

Brolga

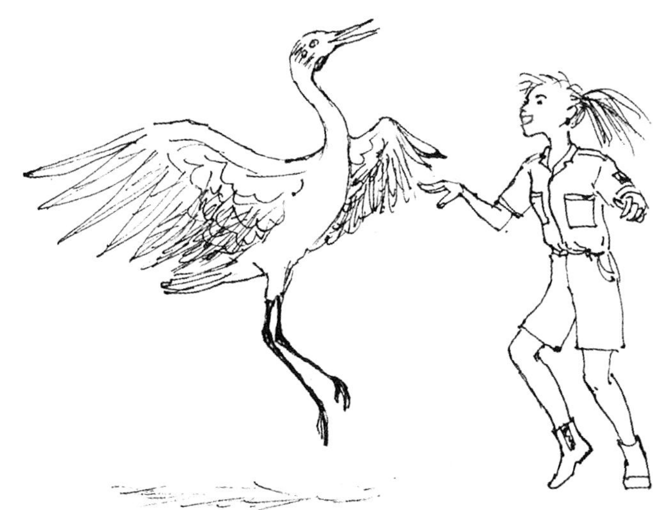

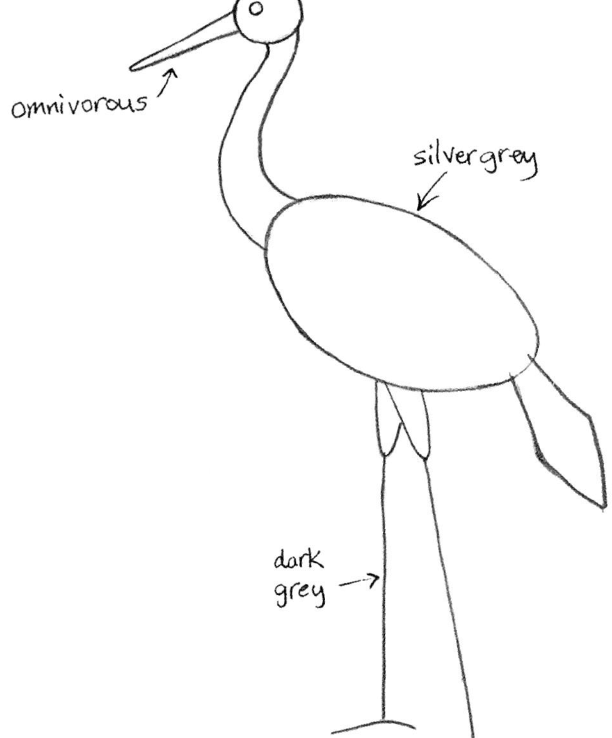

omnivorous

silvergrey

dark grey

spectacular dance display at any time of the year, not just in courtship.

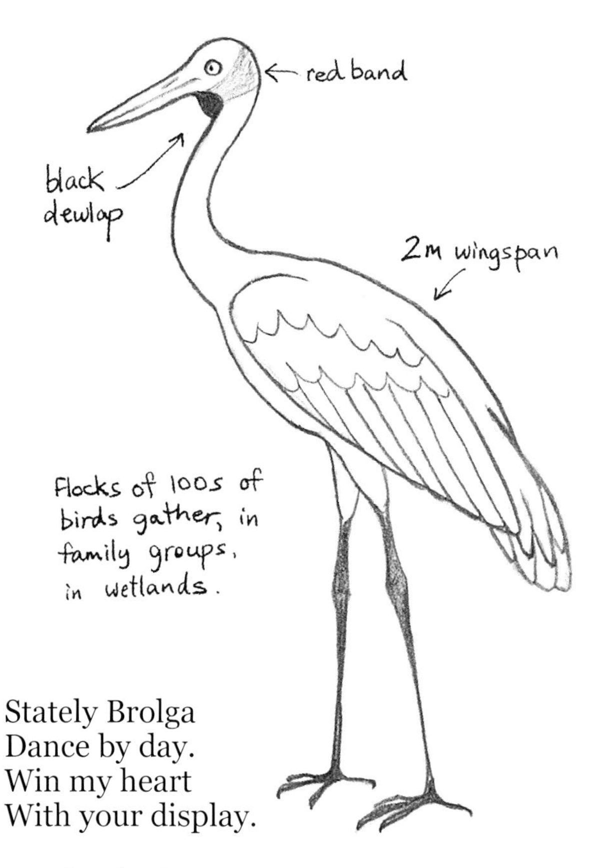

red band

black dewlap

2m wingspan

Flocks of 100s of birds gather, in family groups, in wetlands.

Brolgas mate for life, with both caring for eggs & chicks.

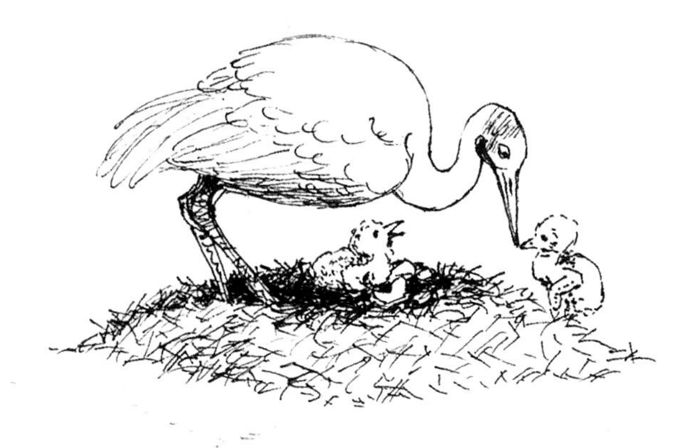

Stately Brolga
Dance by day.
Win my heart
With your display.

On slender legs
You bob & swirl,
For once you were
A lovely girl.*

* from an Aboriginal legend

Superb Lyrebird

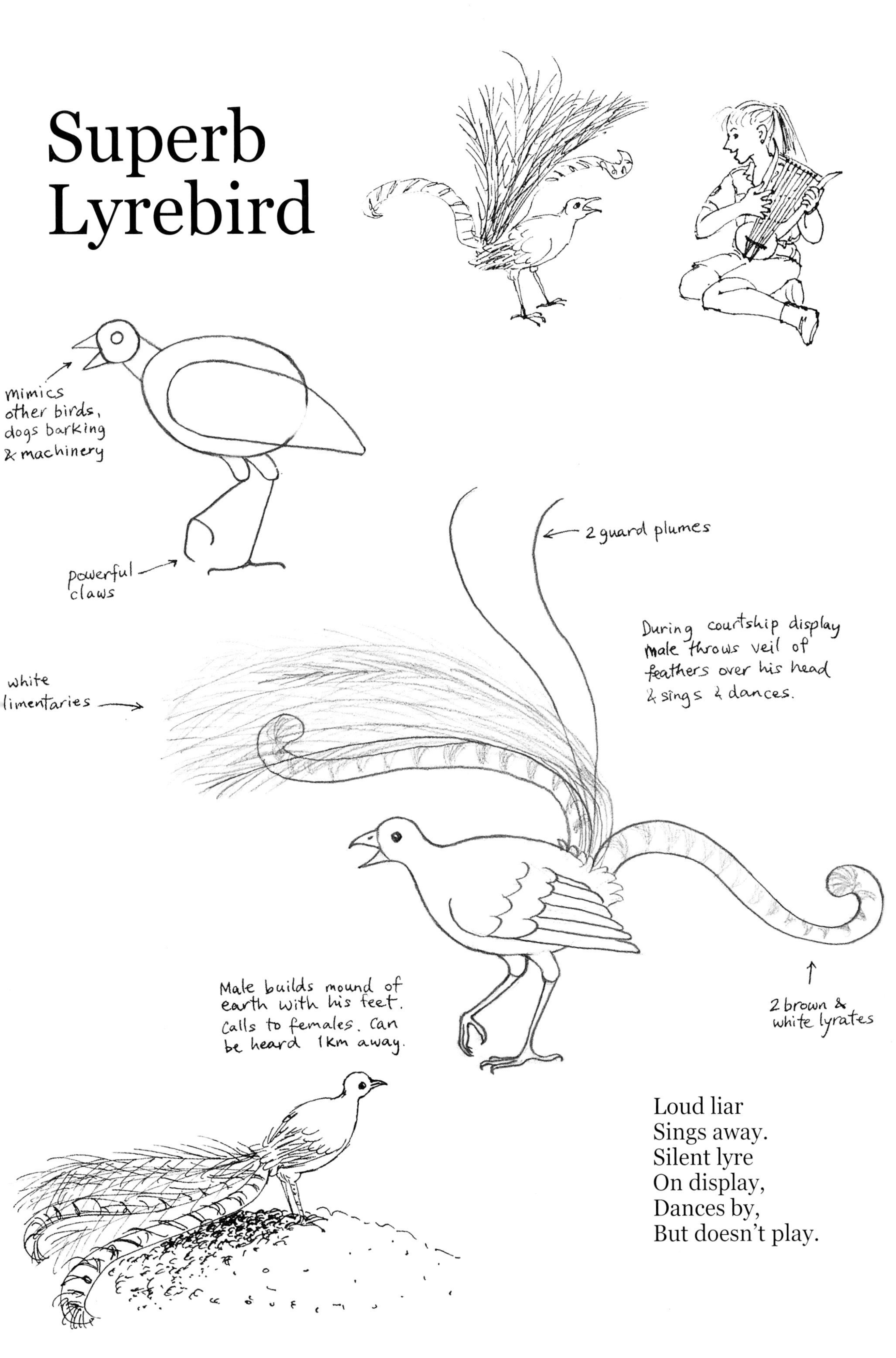

mimics other birds, dogs barking & machinery

powerful claws

white limentaries

2 guard plumes

During courtship display male throws veil of feathers over his head & sings & dances.

Male builds mound of earth with his feet. Calls to females. Can be heard 1km away.

2 brown & white lyrates

Loud liar
Sings away.
Silent lyre
On display,
Dances by,
But doesn't play.

Wedgetailed Eagle

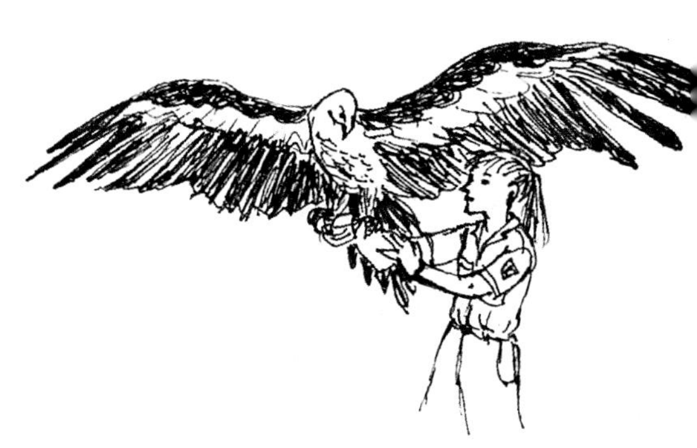

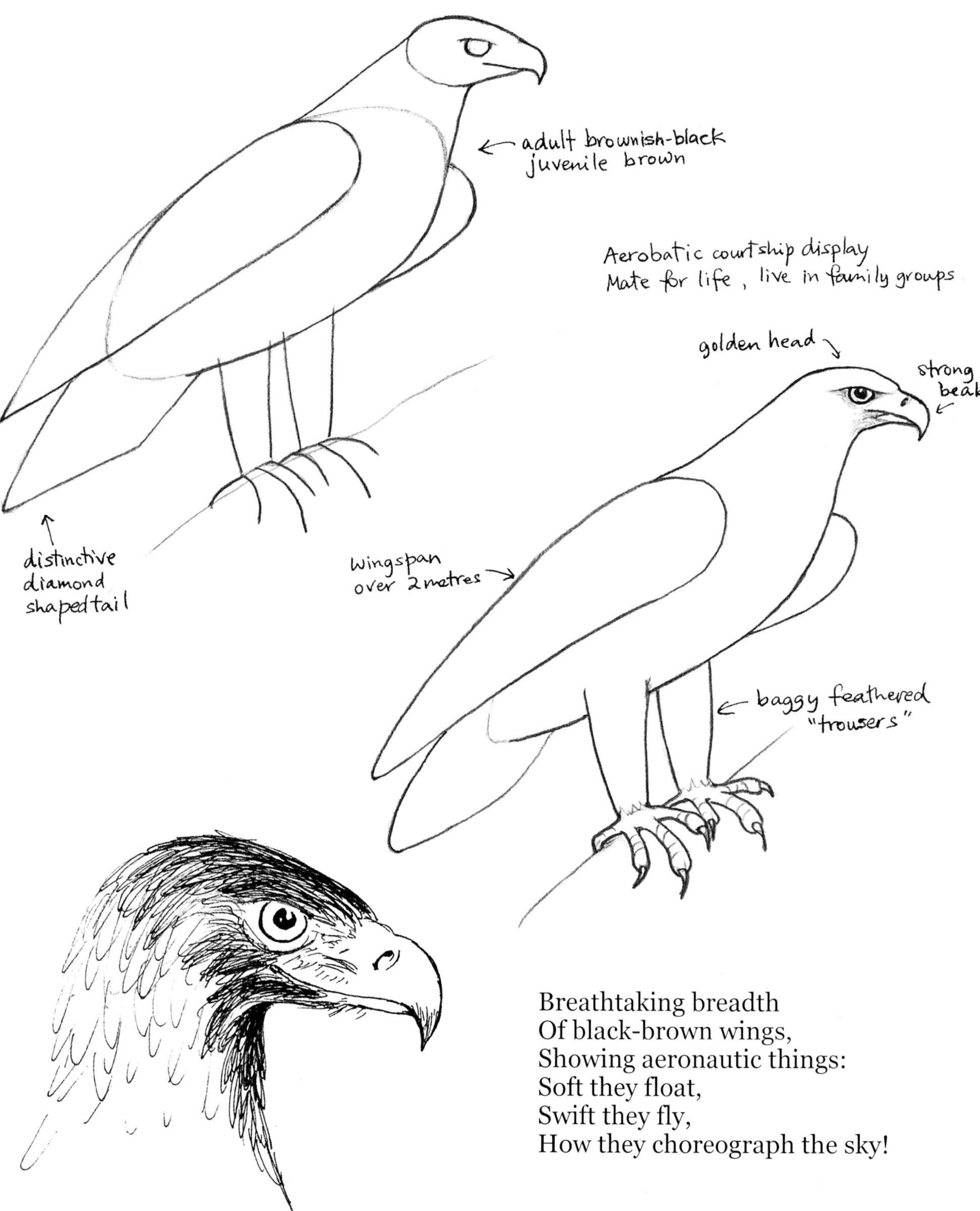

adult brownish-black
juvenile brown

Aerobatic courtship display
Mate for life, live in family groups

distinctive
diamond
shaped tail

golden head

strong
beak

Wingspan
over 2 metres

baggy feathered
"trousers"

Breathtaking breadth
Of black-brown wings,
Showing aeronautic things:
Soft they float,
Swift they fly,
How they choreograph the sky!

Black Currawong

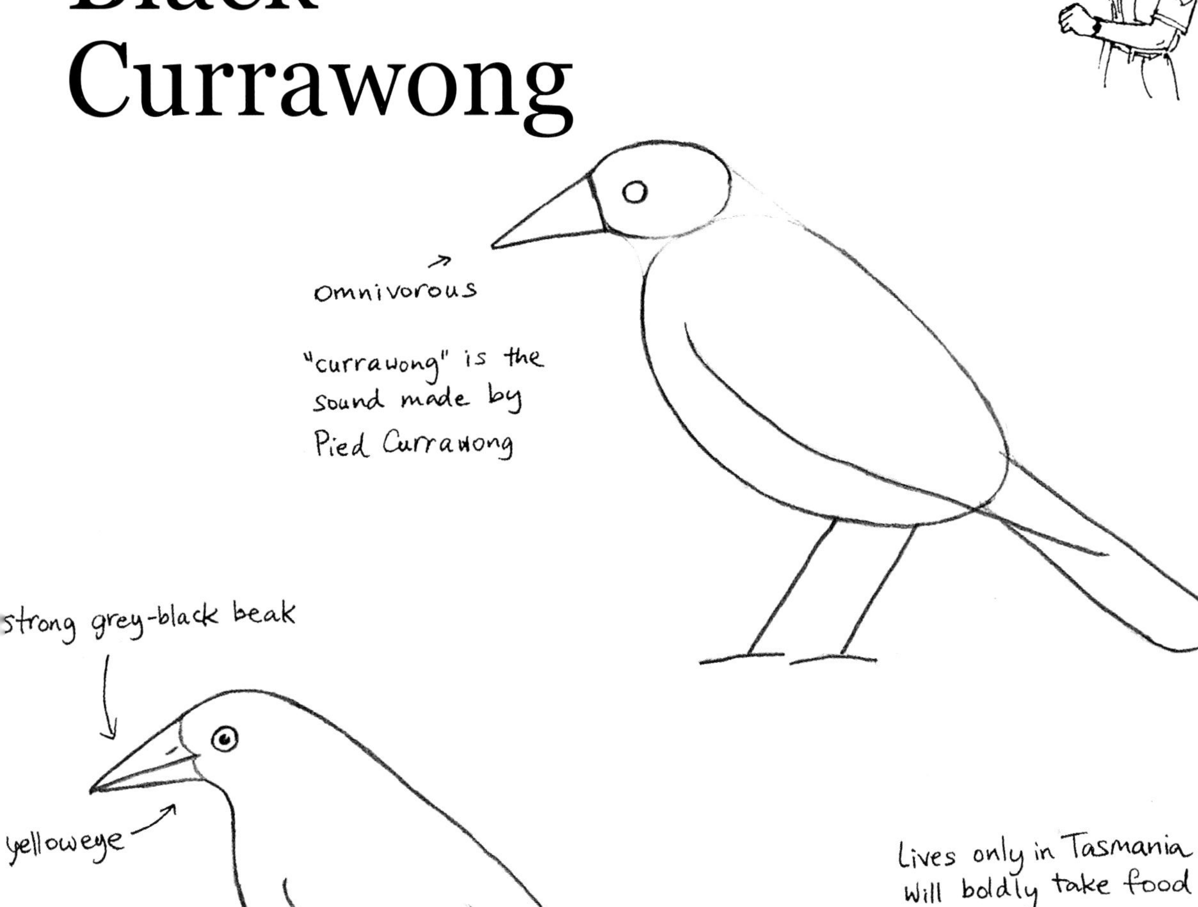

Omnivorous

"currawong" is the sound made by Pied Currawong

strong grey-black beak

yellow eye

Lives only in Tasmania
Will boldly take food from humans.

white tipped wings

← white tipped tail

You beaut
Black suit.
"Curr-a-wong!"
That's my song.

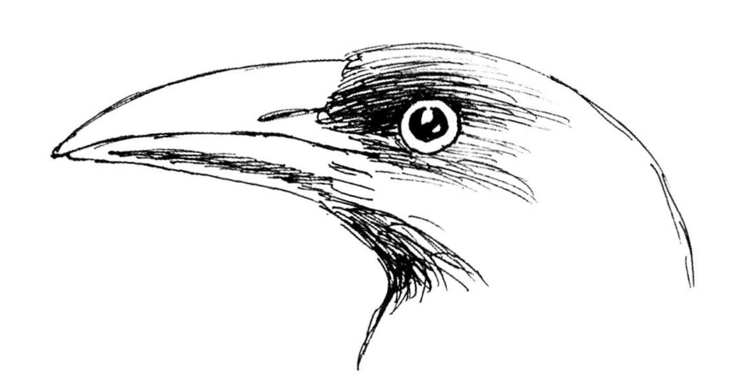

Sydney Funnel Web Spider

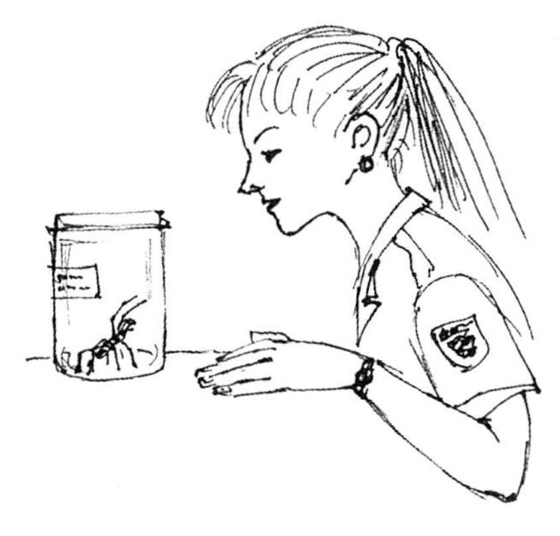

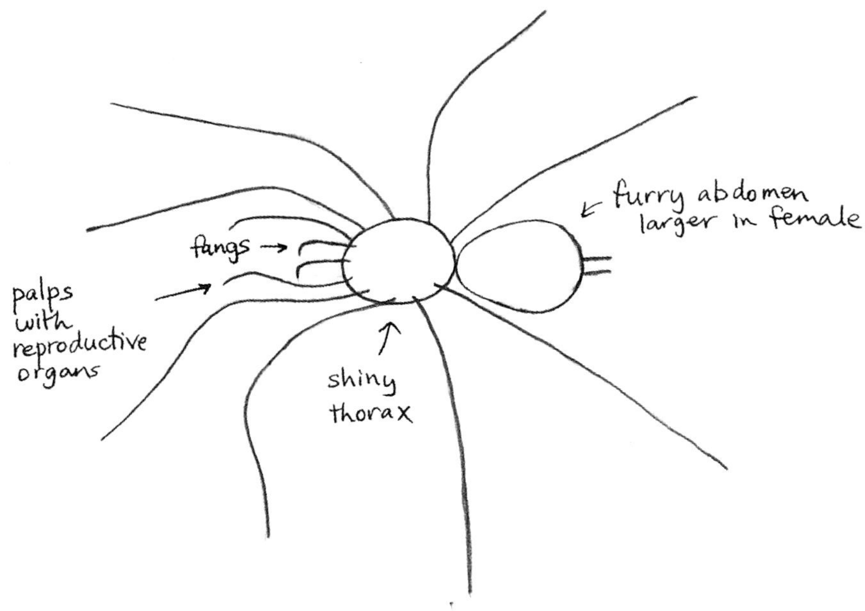

fangs →

palps
with
reproductive
organs

← furry abdomen
larger in female

↑
shiny
thorax

Australia's most dangerous
spider, found within
100 Km of Sydney, the
bite of the male is fatal
within an hour unless
given antivenom.

Males wander into houses
searching for mates

several small
eyes close →
together

↙ 8 hairy legs

←spinnerets

↖mating
spur

claws ↗

Female may live for 20 years,
staying in burrow lined
with silk, raising spiderlings.

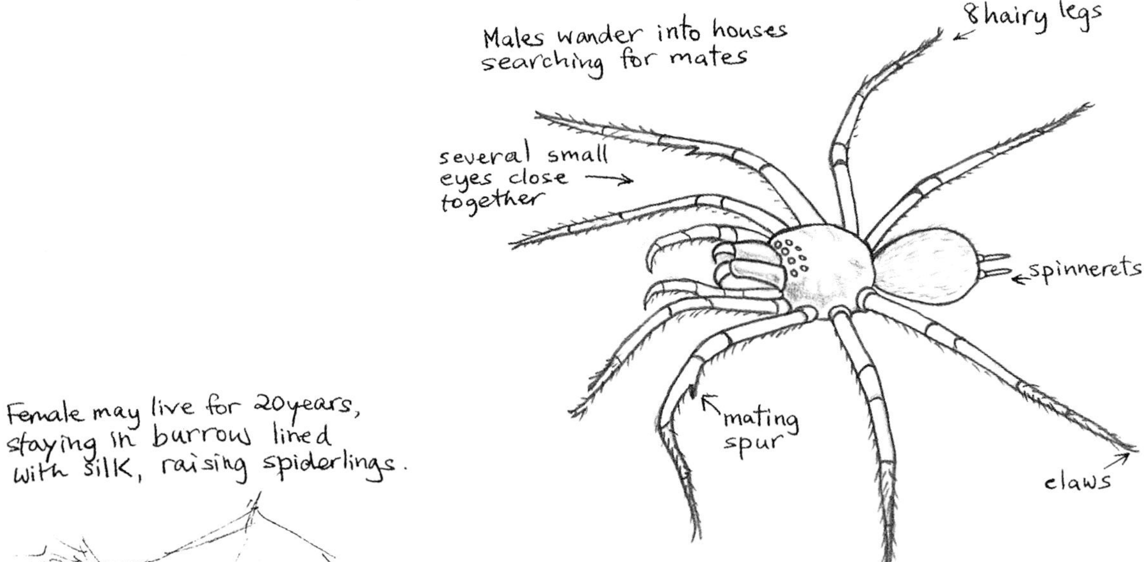

If you live on Sydneyside,
Beware what finds a place to hide
Or slyly slips in for a ride.
Then if it gives a little nip,
You'll need to see the doctor quick.

Blue Ringed Octopus

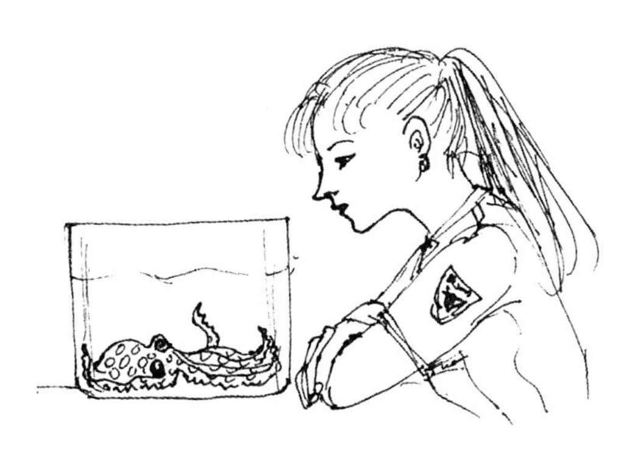

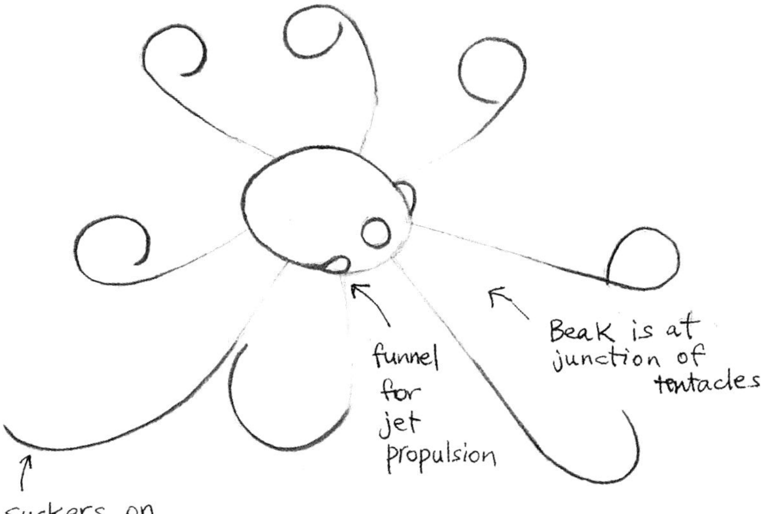

Most dangerous octopus in Australia, bite is fatal.

Poison in saliva immobilises prey, usually crabs & molluscs.

Beak is at junction of tentacles

funnel for jet propulsion

suckers on tentacles attach to rock

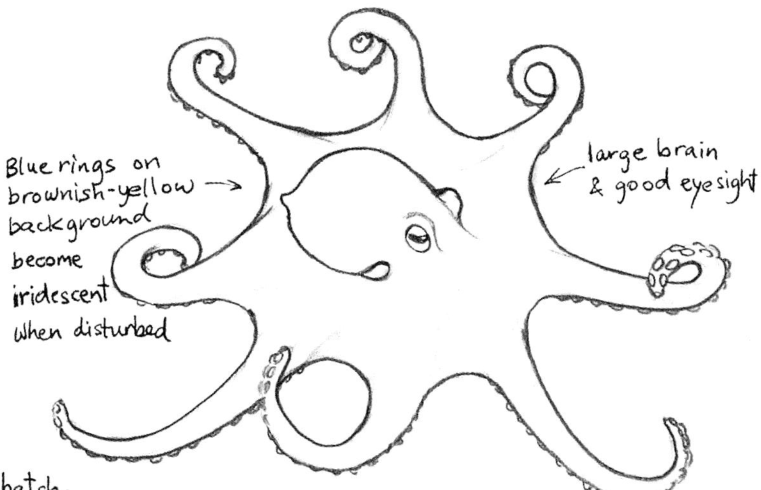

Blue rings on brownish-yellow background become iridescent when disturbed

large brain & good eyesight

Mother carries eggs until they hatch. She dies soon after.

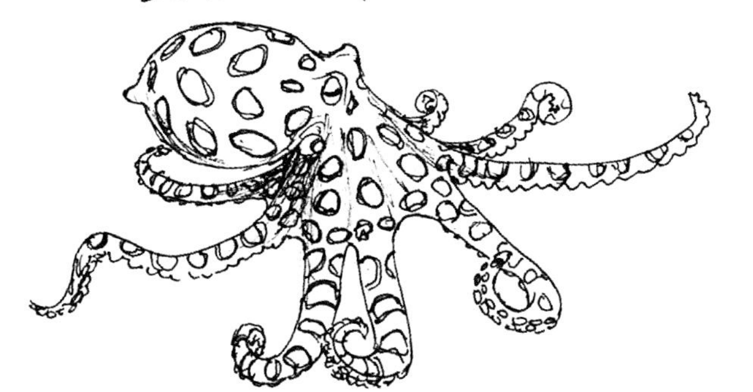

Tempting little rings of blue:
Do not think they are for you!
If you leave them where they lie,
This won't be your turn to die!

Flatback Turtle

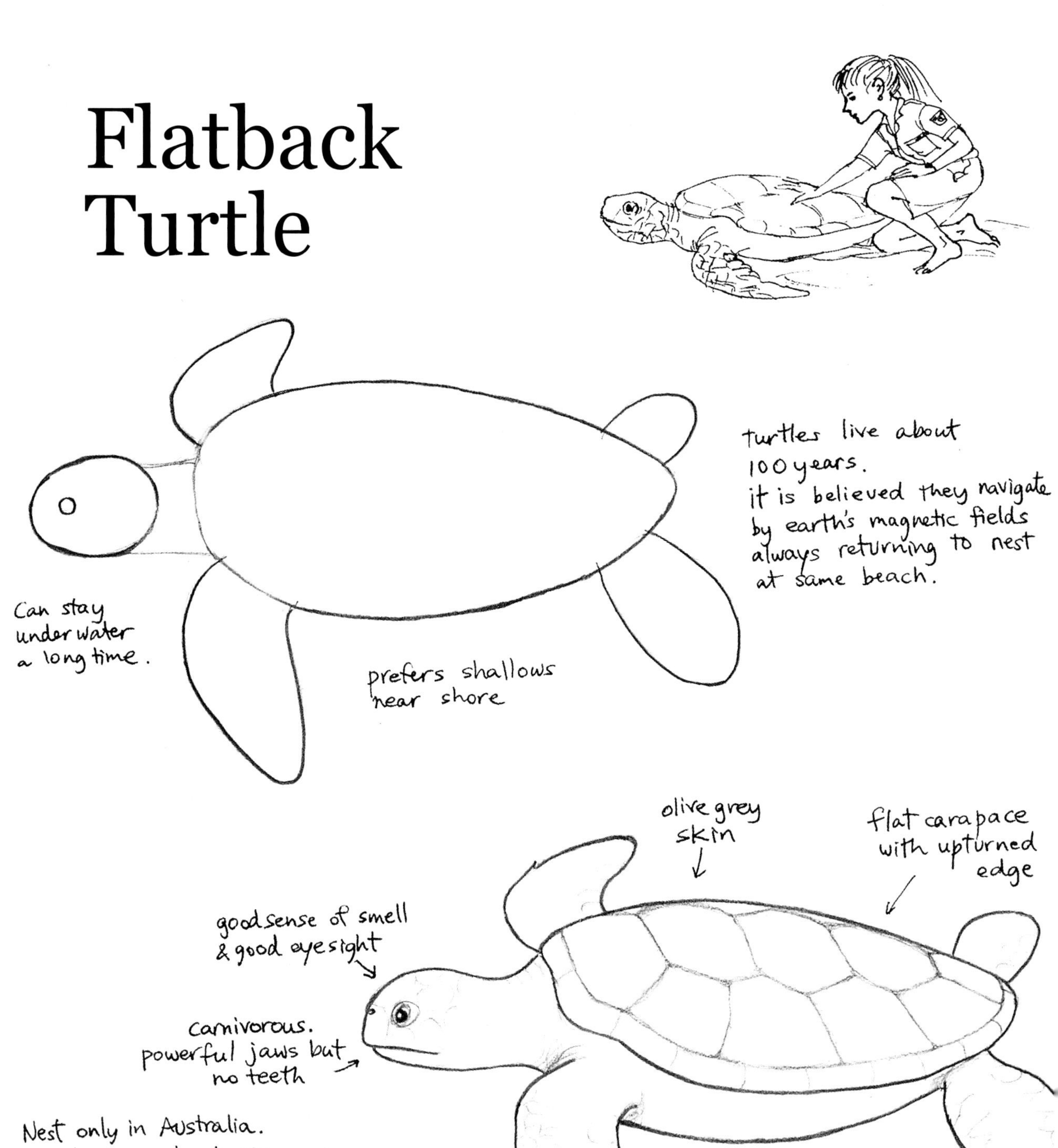

turtles live about 100 years.
it is believed they navigate by earth's magnetic fields always returning to nest at same beach.

Can stay under water a long time.

prefers shallows near shore

olive grey skin

flat carapace with upturned edge

good sense of smell & good eyesight

carnivorous. powerful jaws but no teeth

Nest only in Australia.
Female lays about 50 eggs size of pingpong balls

claw →

powerful flippers

Australia, my only turf,
Carried up, on the surf.
Mind the eggs,
On the beach,
It's hard to keep
Them out of reach.

Weedy Sea
Dragon

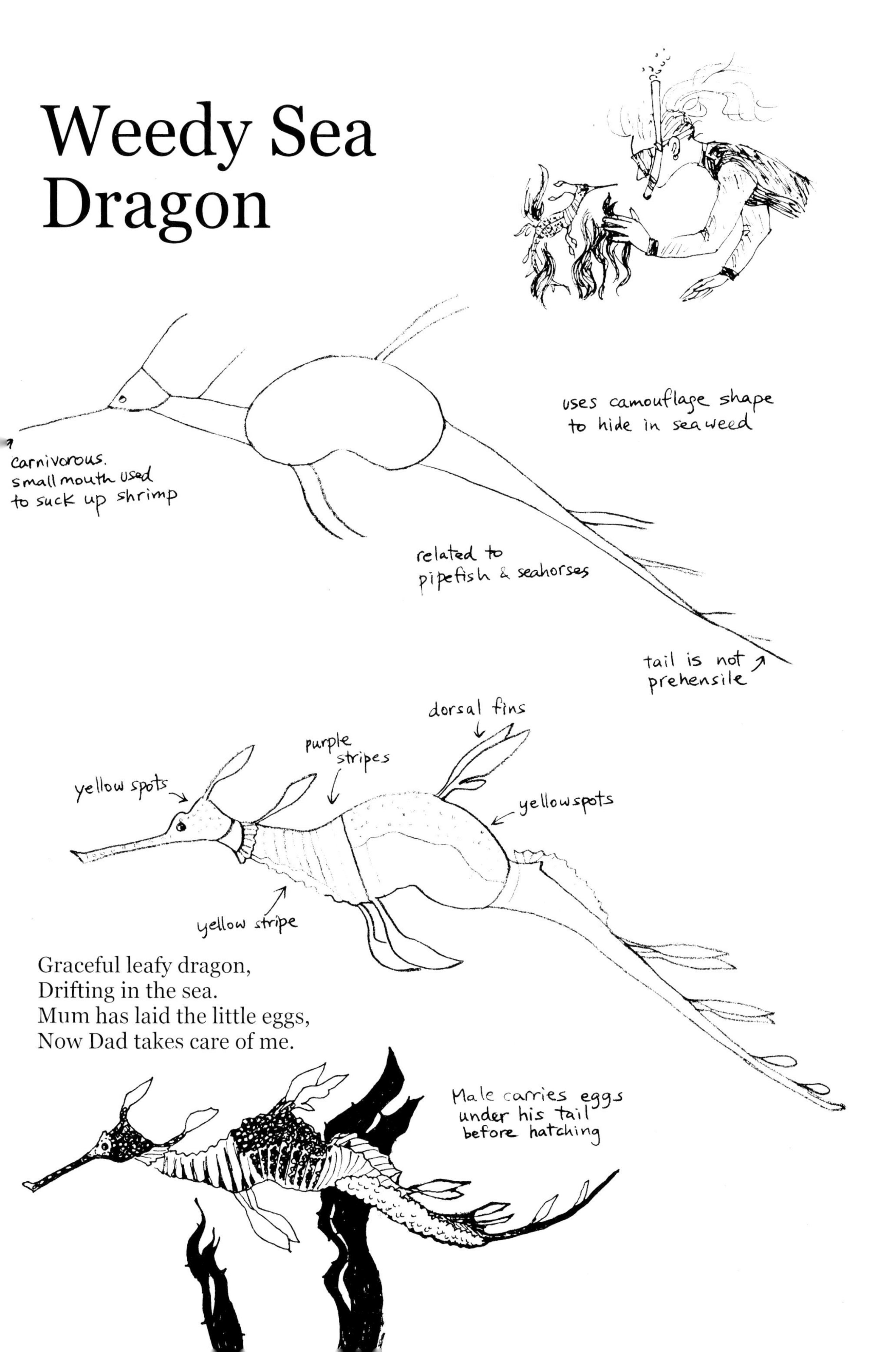

uses camouflage shape
to hide in sea weed

carnivorous.
small mouth used
to suck up shrimp

related to
pipefish & seahorses

tail is not
prehensile

dorsal fins

purple
stripes

yellow spots

yellowspots

yellow stripe

Graceful leafy dragon,
Drifting in the sea.
Mum has laid the little eggs,
Now Dad takes care of me.

Male carries eggs
under his tail
before hatching

Red Handfish

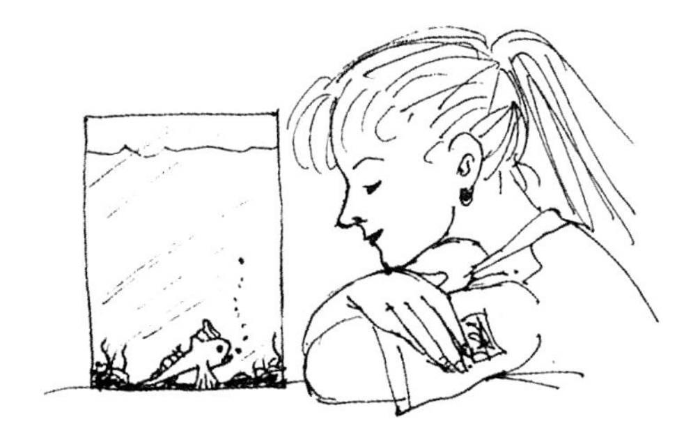

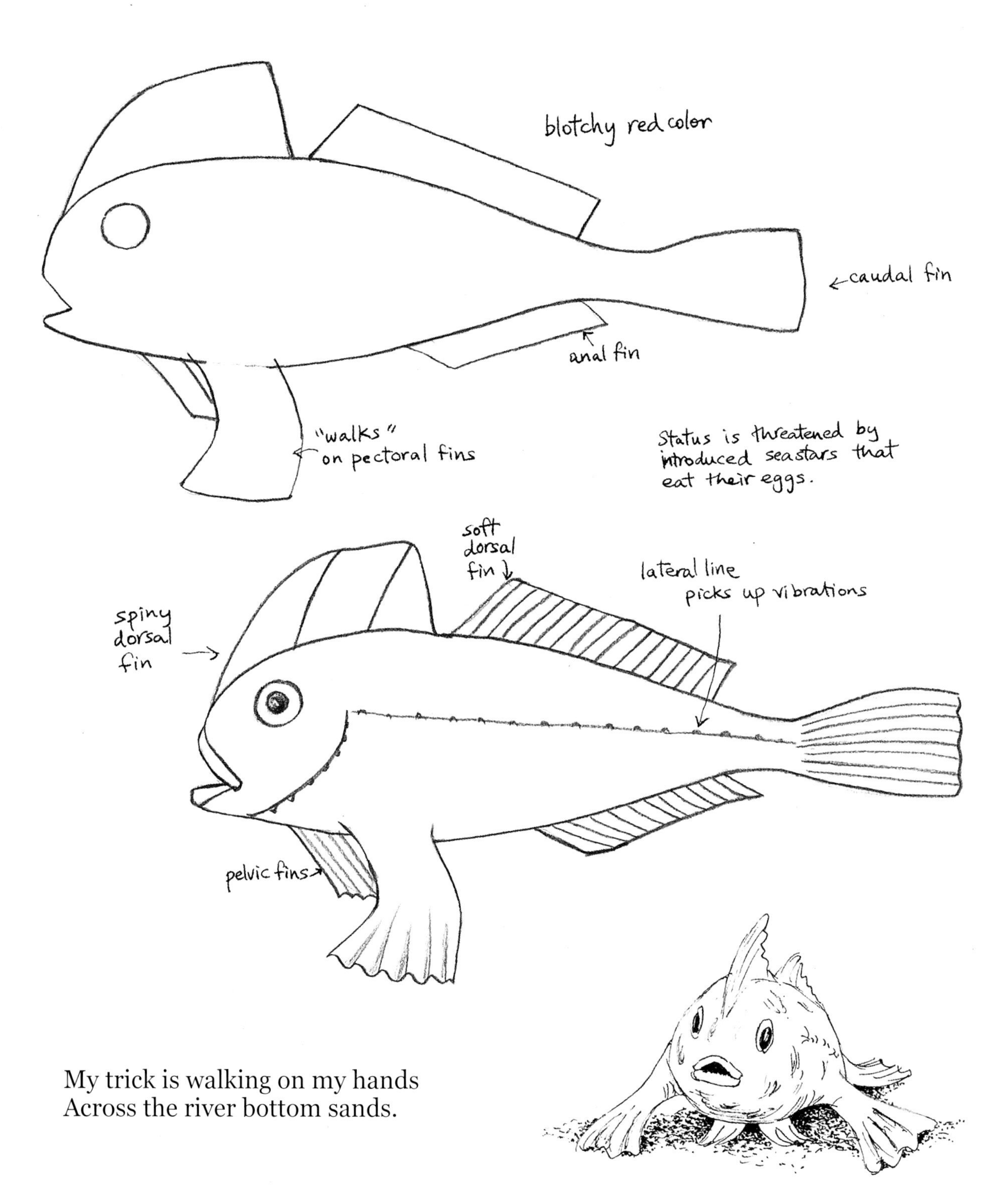

blotchy red color

←caudal fin

anal fin

"walks" on pectoral fins

Status is threatened by introduced seastars that eat their eggs.

soft dorsal fin↓

lateral line picks up vibrations

spiny dorsal fin →

pelvic fins→

My trick is walking on my hands
Across the river bottom sands.

Gurnard
Scorpionfish

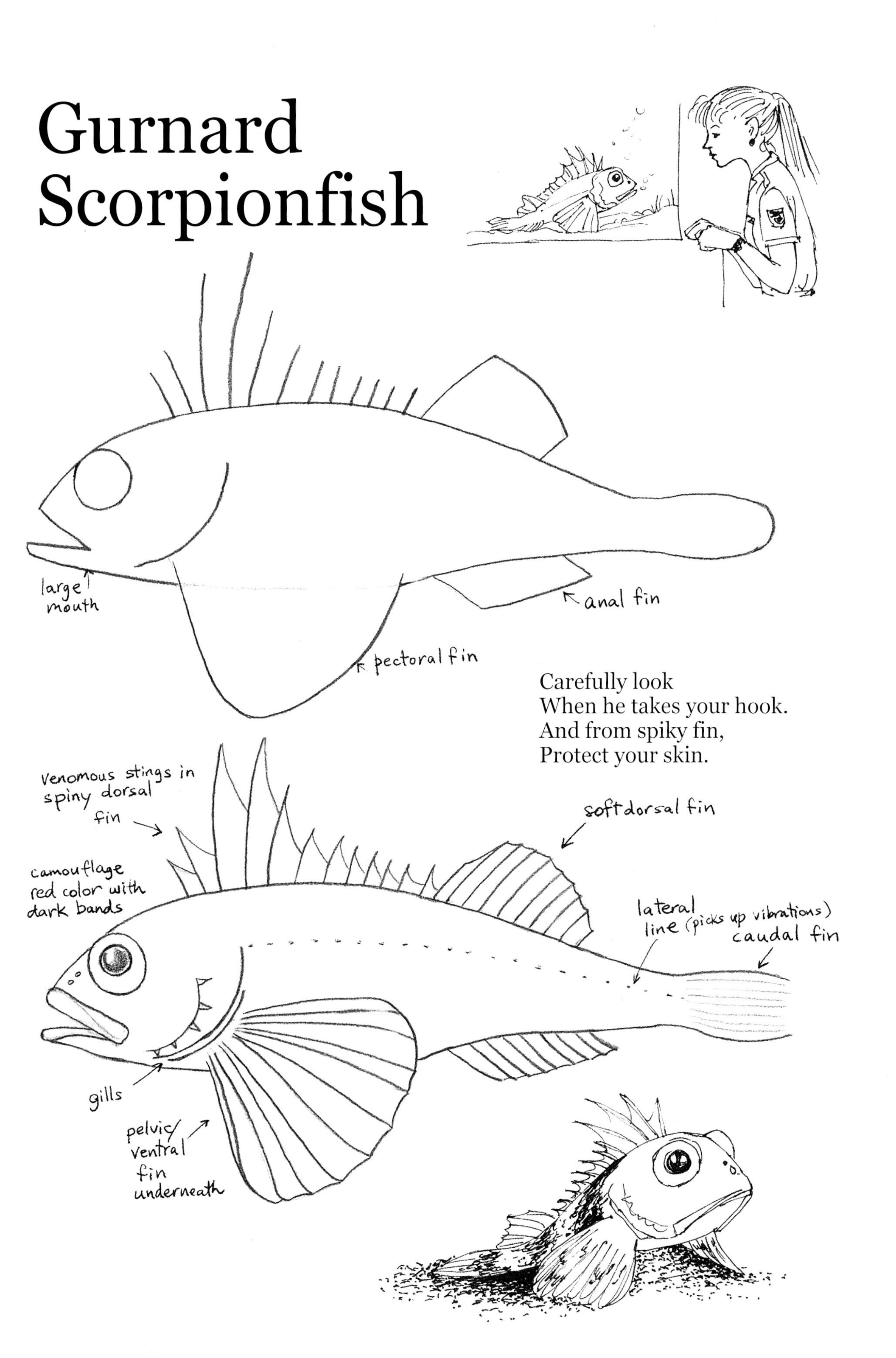

large
mouth

↖ anal fin

↖ pectoral fin

Carefully look
When he takes your hook.
And from spiky fin,
Protect your skin.

venomous stings in
spiny dorsal
fin →

camouflage
red color with
dark bands

soft dorsal fin

lateral
line (picks up vibrations)
caudal fin

gills

pelvic/
ventral
fin
underneath

Crossback Stingaree

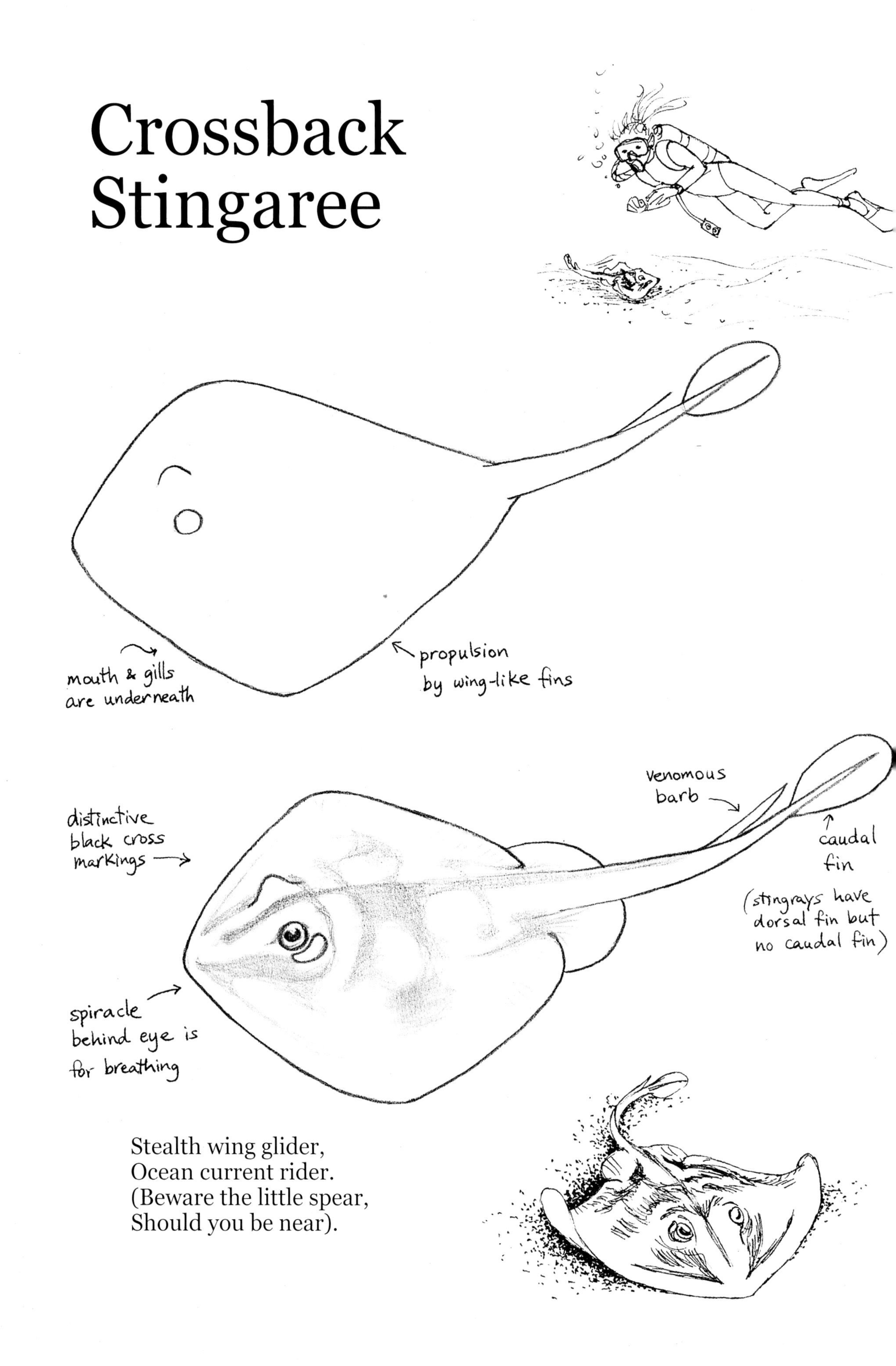

mouth & gills
are underneath

propulsion
by wing-like fins

distinctive
black cross
markings →

spiracle
behind eye is
for breathing

Venomous
barb

↑
caudal
fin

(stingrays have
dorsal fin but
no caudal fin)

Stealth wing glider,
Ocean current rider.
(Beware the little spear,
Should you be near).